THE PIANO MAN

When somebody has an accident, there are sometimes two kinds of injury. One is an injury to the body, perhaps a broken arm or a leg, or something worse. But there is also another kind of injury, and you cannot see these injuries because they are inside a person's head. The shock of a bad accident can do strange and terrible things to a person's brain.

Avril is a nurse in a hospital. She is very good with patients like the man from the sea. He was on a beach, in wet clothes, and nobody knows anything about him, not even his name. He has an injury to his head, but it is not a bad one. He can eat, and drink, and see, and hear. But he cannot speak, and he is very unhappy. Why? What happened to him, and where did he come from?

One day he draws a picture of a piano, so Avril gives him a name – the Piano Man. Somebody, somewhere, knows something about the Piano Man. But that person is on a boat, and the boat is sailing back to St Petersburg in Russia . . .

OXFORD BOOKWORMS LIBRARY
Human Interest

The Piano Man

Stage 1 (400 headwords)

Series Editor: Jennifer Bassett
Founder Editor: Tricia Hedge
Activities Editors: Jennifer Bassett and Christine Lindop

TIM VICARY

The Piano Man

Illustrated by
Owen Freeman

OXFORD UNIVERSITY PRESS

OXFORD
UNIVERSITY PRESS

Great Clarendon Street, Oxford, OX2 6DP, United Kingdom

Oxford University Press is a department of the University of Oxford.
It furthers the University's objective of excellence in research, scholarship,
and education by publishing worldwide. Oxford is a registered trade
mark of Oxford University Press in the UK and in certain other countries

ISBN: 978 0 19 478610 2

A complete recording of this Bookworms edition of
The Piano Man is available in an audio pack. ISBN: 978 0 19 478602 7

Printed in China

Word count (main text): 6,476

For more information on the Oxford Bookworms Library,
visit www.oup.com/bookworms

ACKNOWLEDGEMENTS
Illustrations by: Owen Freeman/Killington Arts

CONTENTS

CHAPTER 1

THE MAN FROM THE SEA

—

The boat, the boat . . . where is it? I must find the boat . . . I'm cold . . . so cold. Oh, Lida, where are you? How can I find you? I must find you . . . So cold, so cold . . . I must get back on the boat . . . Oh, Lida . . . Lida . . . Lida . . .

'Mummy, look at that man!'

'What man?

'That man, there, by the sea! Look, his clothes are all wet!'

'Well, perhaps he went into the sea for a swim.'

'But he's wearing a shirt and trousers and shoes, Mum. Nobody swims in clothes like that!'

Linda Jones and her daughter Ann were on a beach by the sea in the south of England. It was eight o'clock in the morning. It was a sunny day, but cold – not weather for swimming.

Linda Jones looked at the man. Her daughter was right, the man's clothes were not clothes for swimming in. They weren't even summer clothes, they were work clothes – black trousers, a white shirt, and black shoes.

'He does look strange,' she said. 'But people sometimes do strange things, Ann.'

'But Mummy, perhaps he's ill. He's trying to walk –
look! There's something wrong with him!'

The little girl was right. The man stood up, and began
to walk along the beach, by the sea. But he didn't walk
very well. First he walked up the beach, then down
again, to the sea. He fell down, and got up again. Then
he walked into the sea, and fell down again. This time he
didn't get up. He stayed there, lying in the sea.

'You're right, Ann,' Linda said. 'There's something
wrong with that man. You stay here. I'm going to look
at him.'

She walked down the beach to the sea. The man didn't
get up, he stayed lying in the water. Linda stood by the
sea and looked at him. He was a tall young man, about
twenty-five years old, with long dark hair. His clothes
were wet, and he looked cold. His face was very white,
but there was a dark red mark over his left eye.

'Hello. Are you all right?' Linda asked.

The man looked at her, but didn't say anything. Linda
tried again. 'You look cold,' she said. 'Do you need help?'

The man didn't speak. He tried to get up, but he fell
down again, in the water.

'Oh dear,' she said. 'You do need help, don't you?'

She took off her shoes and walked into the sea.
She took the man's arm. 'Come on,' she said. 'Try to
stand up.'

She tried to help him up with one hand, and then two.

But it was not easy. He was bigger than her, and she nearly fell into the sea beside him. But then she got him to his feet and helped him walk out of the sea. On the beach, he sat down again. Linda sat down next to him.

'Are you hurt?' she asked. 'Are you not feeling well?'

'Are you hurt?' Linda asked. 'Are you not feeling well?'

The man looked at her with his strange blue eyes. But he didn't say anything.

'What's your name?' Linda said.

The man didn't answer. He turned his face away, and looked at the sea. Linda looked at the mark over his eye.

'Oh dear,' she said. 'I think you need to go to hospital.' She took out her phone and called for an ambulance.

Twenty minutes later an ambulance arrived, and two ambulance men ran down the beach to the man. They looked into his eyes, felt his hands, and asked questions.

'What's your name, sir?' they said.

No answer.

'How did you hurt your head?' they asked. 'Can you move your legs?'

No answer.

One of the ambulance men turned to Linda Jones.

'Do you know this man?' he asked.

'No,' said Linda. 'He was like this when I found him.'

Suddenly the man stood up, and tried to walk away, back into the sea. But he couldn't walk well. He fell down and lay on the beach. The sea came over his legs. All his clothes were wet and he was very cold.

'Come on, sir,' the ambulance man said. 'You're not well; you need help. We're taking you to the hospital.'

The two ambulance men helped him up and carried him into the ambulance.

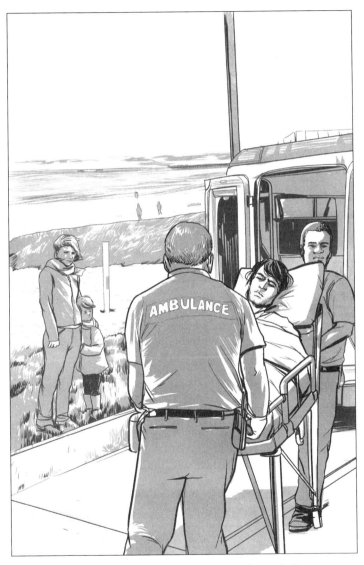

The ambulance men carried him into the ambulance.

At the hospital two nurses took off the man's wet clothes and put him in a warm bed. A young doctor came to look at him. He saw the mark on the man's face, and his cold white hands.

'What happened to you?' the doctor asked. 'How did you hurt your head?'

The man closed his eyes and did not answer.

'Who is he?' the doctor asked the nurses.

'We don't know. He didn't speak to the ambulance men,' a nurse said. 'I asked his name but he didn't say anything. I think he's in shock.'

'Let's have another look at his head.' The doctor moved his fingers carefully over the man's head. 'Ah,' he said. 'There's another injury. Here, under the hair. See? Something hit him very hard here.'

The doctor felt the man's cold hands and feet. 'How long was he in the sea, do you know?'

'We don't know, doctor. We don't know anything about him, because he's not speaking.'

'Well, that can wait. First, we must get him warm. He's too cold. Give him lots of warm drinks, and check him every hour. Let him sleep, but keep him warm all the time. Tomorrow morning he must have a scan for that head injury.'

CHAPTER 2

THE MAN WITH NO NAME

—

*Where am I? All these lights . . . So many people . . .
white coats . . . talking, talking . . . I don't want to
hear them, I don't understand their words . . . I
must find Lida, I must help her . . . How can I find
her? I cannot live without her, my Lida, my song
bird . . .*

The hospital day starts very early. At seven o'clock
the nurses took the man downstairs for his scan.
By nine o'clock he was back in bed on the ward, and a
different doctor came to see him.

'Well, good news, young man,' the doctor said. 'Your
head injury is not very bad. You're going to be fine. How
are you feeling now?'

The man did not answer. He sat up in bed, and looked
at the doctor, and then at the nurse. Then he turned his
face away and stared out of the window.

'Mmm,' said the doctor. He took out a pen, and
slowly moved it from side to side in front of the man's
face. The man's eyes did not move.

'Shock,' said the doctor. 'Shock can do this to the
brain sometimes. And then it can forget how to speak.'
He turned to the nurse. 'Is he saying anything to you?'

'No, not a word,' the nurse said.

'Is he eating and drinking all right?'

'Yes, no problems there,' said the nurse.

'Well, call me when the police arrive. Somebody's coming at midday to ask questions.'

'Why?' said the nurse. 'The poor man is ill.'

'He's a man with no name, no papers, nothing. Where did he come from? The police want to know.'

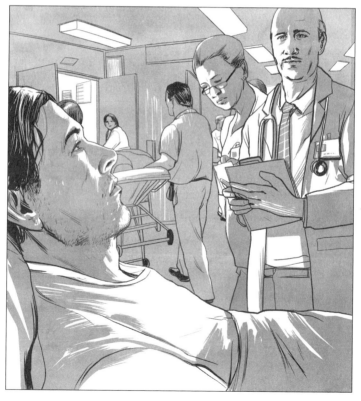

'How are you feeling now?' said the doctor.

When the policeman arrived, the nurse took him to her patient.

'Please be gentle,' she said. 'He has a head injury, and we think he's still in shock after his accident.'

'Good afternoon, sir,' the policeman said to the man in the bed. 'I need to ask you some questions, please. What's your name, and where are you from?'

The policeman held his pen, ready to write down the answers. But there were no answers.

He tried again. 'Why were you on the beach yesterday? Why were your clothes wet? Did you fall off a boat?'

No answer. The man closed his eyes and turned his face to the wall.

'How did you hurt your head? Did somebody hit you?'

No answer.

The policeman spoke more loudly. 'Come on now. WHAT'S YOUR NAME?'

The nurse and the doctor then arrived.

'What are you doing?' said the nurse. 'There's no need to shout. He can hear very well.'

'But he's not answering my questions,' the policeman said. 'Who he is? Where does he come from?'

'We don't know,' said the doctor. 'Can't the questions wait for a day or two? Let him rest now.'

They moved away from the patient's bed.

'I need a name,' the policeman said. 'I can put a name through the police computer. Where does he come from?

Is he an illegal immigrant? Did he fall off a boat full
of illegal immigrants? We need to know these things.
Without a name, I can't do anything. Is he even English?
Was there nothing in the pockets of his clothes?'

'Where are his clothes?' said the doctor.

'I can find them, I think,' the nurse said. She went
away and came back a few minutes later with the man's
clothes. They were white with salt from the sea water.

There was nothing in the pockets, no papers, nothing
with a name on.

'What about the labels in the clothes?' the policeman
said. 'They can sometimes tell you something.'

The nurse found a label in the back of the shirt.

'Look,' she said.

'That's not English,' the doctor said. 'Can you read
it, nurse?'

'No,' the nurse said. 'It looks like some Eastern
European language. Russian, perhaps?'

'Maybe,' the policeman said. 'So perhaps your patient
isn't English. He can't answer the questions because he
doesn't understand them.'

'Mmm,' said the doctor. 'I think he's not answering
because he can't speak. In any language. Something
happened to him. We don't know what, but it was bad.'

'I can bring a police interpreter tomorrow,' said the
policeman. 'He can try a few languages on him. And
now I must go and ask a lot of questions about boats

The nurse found a label in the back of the shirt.

and ships near here yesterday. Perhaps he fell off a boat, and somebody is looking for him.'

The policeman left, but there was no rest yet for the man from the sea. It was a busy hospital, with accidents coming in all the time.

'We can't keep him in this ward tonight,' the doctor said. 'We need the bed. Take him over to the Psychiatric Unit. They can give him a bed for a few nights. Perhaps they can help him with speaking. Ask for nurse Avril O'Brien. She's very good with patients like these.'

CHAPTER 3

THE PIANO

—

*My head feels better today . . . My eyes still hurt,
but I can see better . . . These people are kind, but I
cannot talk to them . . . What can I say? What can I
tell them? I do not want to live without Lida . . .
and Lida is lost to me for ever . . . nothing matters
now, nothing . . .*

The Psychiatric Unit was a new part of the hospital.
It had nice rooms for the patients, with pictures on
the walls. There was a patients' sitting room with books,
some comfortable chairs, and an old piano. Outside,
there was a small garden with flowers.

Patients here had mental problems of different kinds.
Many of them were older people; some of them did not
know the day of the week, or their own names.

Avril O'Brien was very good with these patients. She
was kind and friendly. She liked to sit with her patients
or walk with them in the little garden. She talked to them
all the time. Sometimes they answered, and sometimes
they didn't. But that didn't matter to Avril. She just went
on talking in her warm Irish voice.

She was very interested in the new patient – the man
from the sea, the man with no name.

'How can I help him best?' she asked Dr Sansom.

Dr Sansom was the doctor in the Psychiatric Unit. He was very good at helping patients with mental health problems. Avril was his best nurse.

'Talk,' he said. 'Just talk to him, Avril. He's not going to answer you, but we want him to listen.'

So Avril talked to him, in her warm Irish voice. She talked about her family, about the weather, about books and films . . . The man from the sea said nothing, and did not answer any of her questions. But he began to listen, and to watch Avril's face when she talked.

In the morning the policeman came back. With him was a tall young woman with black hair, and a big smile.

'Hi! I'm Katya,' she said to Avril.

Avril looked at her in surprise. 'Do you work for the police?' she asked. 'You don't look like police.'

Katya laughed. 'No,' she said. 'I'm an interpreter of Eastern European languages. I work for myself.'

'Our usual man is on holiday,' said the policeman. 'He's always on holiday when you need him. Katya helps us when that happens.'

Avril took them into her patient's room. He lay on his bed and watched them. But when Katya began to speak, he closed his eyes and turned his face to the wall. Katya spoke for three or four minutes in different languages, but the man did not move or open his eyes.

Katya stopped and looked at the policeman. 'I'm

sorry, Ben,' she said. 'I tried Polish, Ukrainian, Russian, and Serbian. He just doesn't want to talk.'

'But did he understand any of those languages?'

'I don't know. How can you tell?' said Katya. 'He's just lying on the bed with his eyes closed.'

'What about that shirt label?' said the policeman. He turned to Avril. 'Have you got his shirt?'

Avril found the shirt and showed it to Katya.

'Yes, this is a Russian name on the label,' she said.

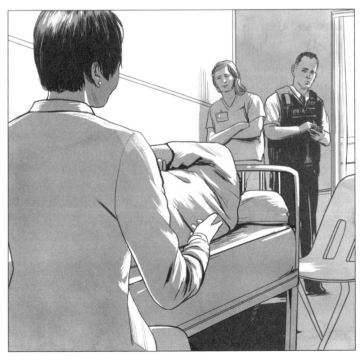

Katya spoke for three or four minutes in different languages.

'So he's Russian then?' the policeman said, happily.

'Maybe,' said Katya. 'But you can find these shirts in Poland, in Latvia, in London, even. This label is a famous shirt maker in St Petersburg.'

'Well, that's no help,' said the policeman. 'Oh dear, this is getting very difficult. He *must* tell us his name. I'm going to talk to him in English again.'

'No, you're not,' said Avril. 'This is my patient, and he is not a well man. He needs to rest, to be quiet. You must leave now.' She opened the door, and they all left the room. Avril closed the door quietly behind her.

Outside the room the policeman turned to Avril. 'So what do we do now, nurse?' he asked.

'Wait,' said Avril.

'OK. But call me when he starts talking, right?'

'Of course,' said Avril. She smiled at Katya, and Katya gave her a big smile back.

Later in the day, Avril went into her patient's room and sat down next to him on the bed. She had a pen and some paper in her hands.

'Listen,' she said. 'You can't talk to me, I know that. But maybe you can write or draw something, can you? Look – like this . . .' She drew a picture on the paper and wrote something next to it.

'See that?' she said. 'That's a picture of me, can't you see? And there's my name beside it. Avril O'Brien, see?'

She laughed. 'It's not a very good picture, I know, but you can see it's me, can't you?'

She gave him the paper and pen. 'Now you. Draw a picture of yourself, and write your name beside it.'

Then she sat quietly and watched.

The man took the pen and paper from her, but for a long time he sat very still, and did nothing. Avril watched him with a friendly smile on her face.

Avril sat quietly and watched.

'Go on,' she said kindly. 'You can do it. It's paper, it can't hurt you. Draw a picture. Do it for me.'

The man looked at the paper again. Then he started to draw. His hand moved quickly across the paper. Avril sat still and watched him. It was very quiet in the room, and she could hear the sound of the pen on the paper. Then she heard another sound. It was the sound of crying.

He finished the drawing and looked up. There were tears on his face. Avril took the paper from his hand.

It was a drawing of a piano.

'That's beautiful!' she said. 'A piano! Do you like piano music? Do you play the piano, maybe?'

No answer. The man stared down at his hands. He did not look at Avril.

Avril laughed. 'Well, that's wonderful, so it is! Come with me, young man. I have something to show you!'

She put down the paper, and held out her hand. The man got out of bed, and went with Avril into the patients' sitting room. It was his first time in here.

'Look!' Avril said. 'We have a piano here! One of our old patients gave it to us. Come, play something for me.'

The man sat in front of the piano. Avril pulled up a chair and sat next to the piano. For a long time he did nothing. He sat still and looked at the piano. Then, very slowly, he pressed one of the white piano keys with his finger. Avril watched and waited.

But there was no music. The man just played one

note, pressing the same key with the same finger. He played the note again, and again, and again – more and more quickly, louder and louder and LOUDER!

Then he stopped. Tears ran down his face. He put his face in his hands, and whispered one word, 'Lida . . . Lida . . . Lida!' Then he got up suddenly, and walked quickly out of the room. He went back to his bed, and lay on it, face down, with his hands over the back of his head.

Avril went to find Dr Sansom.

'He spoke!' she told him. 'He said one word, over and over again, but I didn't hear it very well. It sounded like 'leader'. But what can that mean?'

Dr Sansom shook his head. 'Leader? I don't know. But the interesting thing is the piano, Avril. Maybe music is the key. Tomorrow, take him to the piano again.'

He put his face in his hands and whispered one word . . .

CHAPTER 4

THE MUSIC

—

How can I play music without Lida? . . . Music was my life . . . Now it is my death . . . The sound of one note on the piano goes through me like a knife . . . Oh, why did I swim to land? . . . Why didn't the sea take me down, down, down . . . to sleep the long sleep . . .

The next morning Avril took her patient into the sitting room. He sat at the piano but he did not touch the keys. His face was closed; his eyes saw nothing.

'You're a long way away, Mr Piano Man,' Avril said to him, smiling. 'Where are you now? Are you thinking about your home, about your family?'

No answer.

Avril took some photographs out of her bag. 'Would you like to see some photos of my family, Mr Piano Man?' she said. 'Look, here's my husband, Gerry. I told you about him yesterday. And this is my son Ryan. He's sixteen now. He's a big boy, taller than me. He loves playing football. And this is my daughter Mary. She's fourteen. She loves music; she listens to it all the time.'

One by one she gave the photos to the Piano Man. He looked at them, and then gave them back to her.

'Oh, here's one to show you. This is Mary when she was little. About eight, I think. She's having a piano lesson. But she stopped lessons after two years. So sad, I love listening to piano music.'

The Piano Man held the photo of Mary and looked at it for a long minute. His face did not change, but suddenly he put the photo down, turned round to the piano, and began to play.

It was a happy piece of music, light and easy. Avril laughed.

'Oh, how wonderful! I know that! My Mary played

The Piano Man turned round to the piano and began to play.

that piece. Well, she didn't really play it, but she tried to learn it. You play it so well!'

The Piano Man stopped playing. Avril watched him.

'Can you play some more music for us?' she asked.

She looked round the sitting room. There was another patient, sitting at the back of the room. This was Doris, a very old lady. Sometimes Doris remembered things; sometimes she didn't.

'I think Doris is enjoying your music,' Avril said.

The Piano Man looked round. Doris nodded and smiled at him. The Piano Man turned back to the piano and began to play.

This was a very different piece of music, fast and exciting, full of colour and life. The Piano Man's eyes were closed. His body moved to the music, and his fingers danced over the keys. Avril watched his hands.

'You're a musician, aren't you?' she said. 'A pianist.'

All that day the Piano Man was in and out of the sitting room. Sometimes he just sat at the piano; sometimes he played – fast exciting music, slow sad music. Then he went back to his room, and lay on his bed, with his hands over his head. Then back to the piano again . . .

Dr Sansom came to listen to him. 'You're right, Avril,' he said. 'He's a wonderful musician. The music is talking through him. There's a change coming. Leave him alone, and wait.'

Late in the afternoon, the Piano Man went to the piano again, and began to play a new piece of music. It was slow, very beautiful music, like a song. Avril sat with him for a time, then stood up.

'Don't stop,' she whispered. 'I must see another patient for a few minutes. Back soon.'

She went quietly out of the room. Doris was still in her usual chair at the back of the room, smiling and nodding to the music.

Avril was with the other patient for ten minutes, then went back to the sitting room. She heard Doris's voice.

'Nurse, nurse! Come quick!'

'What is it, Doris? What's the matter?'

'Look!' said Doris. 'He's crying. Poor boy!'

The Piano Man sat at the piano, with his face in his hands. Tears ran between his fingers and down the backs of his hands.

'Poor boy,' said Doris. 'Poor boy, poor boy.'

'Yes, all right, Doris,' Avril said. 'I'm here now.' She put her hand very gently on the Piano Man's arm.

'He wants a cup of tea,' said Doris loudly. 'Poor boy.'

'Yes, you're right,' Avril said.

She went quickly to the nurses' kitchen, and came back with a large hot mug of tea. Gently, she took the Piano Man's hands away from his face, and gave him the mug of tea.

'There,' she said. 'Drink some tea. Tea always helps.'

'Drink some tea,' Avril said. 'Tea always helps.'

The Piano Man's hands closed around the hot mug. He looked up into Avril's face. '*Spasibo*,' he whispered.

Before she went home, Avril went to the computer in the nurses' room. 'Now, what was that word?' she thought. 'Spas–something. Spassee . . .' She tried the spelling spasseeba – and Google found the word for her at once.

Spasibo was 'thank you' in Russian.

CHAPTER 5

LUDMILLA

—

When Lida and I made music, it was like falling in love every time – the piano with the voice, the voice with the piano. How can I live without Lida, without music? I am nothing, just a poor half thing, a garden without flowers, a sky without the sun . . .

When she arrived at work the next morning, Avril looked for Dr Sansom. She wanted to tell him about the Piano Man and the Russian word. But Dr Sansom called her on the phone.

'Ah, Avril,' he said. 'Can you come now? I need you. We've a new patient, a Russian girl. She arrived half an hour ago. I want you to be with her this morning.'

Avril went upstairs to the ward. 'A Russian girl?' she thought. 'Suddenly, everything round here is Russian!'

They went to the new patient's room and looked in through the door. A young woman lay in the bed. Her face looked very white.

Dr Sansom read from the hospital notes on the door.

Ludmilla Terenkova, 22, Russian. Head injury.
Brought in by ambulance from Falmouth, after
an accident on a sailing boat, out at sea.

'She had a small operation three days ago for the head injury,' Dr Sansom told Avril. 'That went well, and the head injury is better now. But there is something wrong. She's crying a lot, and getting very angry. So they sent her to us. Let's go in and talk to her. You speak first.'

They went into the room and stood by the bed. Avril smiled at the young woman.

'Hello, Ludmilla,' she said. 'I'm Avril O'Brien, and this is Dr Sansom. How are you feeling now?'

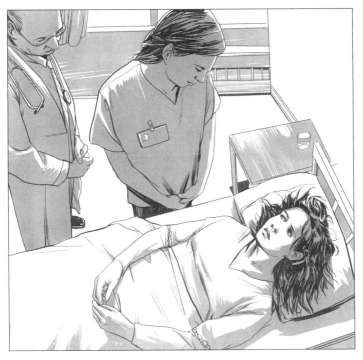

'Hello, Ludmilla,' Avril said.

Ludmilla looked at her. She was a very pretty girl, but her face was very white and there were tears in her eyes.

'Do you speak English?' asked Dr Sansom.

Ludmilla nodded. 'A little,' she said.

'Oh, that's good,' said Avril. 'Can you tell us how you hurt your head?' She pulled a chair next to the bed and sat down.

'I was on a boat, out at sea,' Ludmilla said. 'I . . . I fell and I hurt my head. I don't remember very well.'

'No, of course you don't,' said Avril gently. 'But how did you come to the hospital? Do you remember that?'

'I came by ambulance. The boat came into Falmouth, is that the name? Then the ambulance came.'

'And who called the ambulance?' asked Dr Sansom.

'Ivan.'

'And who is Ivan?' asked Avril.

Ludmilla turned her face away from them and for a moment she did not speak. Then she whispered, 'My fiancé. It's his boat. We were . . . we were on holiday.'

Avril and Dr Sansom waited, but Ludmilla did not look at them, or say anything.

'Is Ivan here now?' Avril said. She smiled and looked round the room. 'Did he come with you to the hospital?'

The tears in Ludmilla's eyes began to run down her face. She laughed angrily. 'No. He went back to the boat. He's going back to St Petersburg, he said.' Suddenly, she sat up in bed. 'Please,' she said to Avril. 'Please, I must

talk to my father. He's in St Petersburg now. Please get
my mobile phone from my bag . . . it's very important. I
must talk to him immediately, I must tell him . . .' Tears
ran down her face, and she tried to get out of bed.

Avril quickly put her hand on Ludmilla's arm, and
helped her back into bed.

'Shhh,' she said gently. 'It's all right, don't cry. Of
course you can call your father. But first, you must stay
in bed and rest a little.'

'No. Ivan went back to the boat,' Ludmilla said.

She looked up at Dr Sansom.

Dr Sansom nodded. 'Yes, rest is important, because of your head injury. Nurse O'Brien is going to get you something now, to help you sleep. Everything's going to be all right, Ms Terenkova. We're here to help you.'

Outside the patient's room, Dr Sansom said, 'Watch her, Avril.' He looked at his watch. 'I must run . . . I have a meeting. Talk to you later.'

It was a busy day for Avril. She had the Piano Man, the Russian girl, and three new patients too. She came often to Ludmilla's room and looked in, but Ludmilla slept most of the day.

In the afternoon Avril looked in again. Ludmilla was not in her bed. Avril went in quickly. Ludmilla was by the window, with her mobile phone. She spoke in Russian, very fast. She finished the call, and turned to Avril. There were angry tears in her eyes.

'Was that your father?' said Avril. 'Is he coming to take you home?'

'No,' Ludmilla said. 'Yes. Maybe . . . I don't know. It's very difficult. My father . . .' She began to cry.

'Tell me about it,' said Avril. 'I'm a good listener.'

'I can't talk about it,' Ludmilla said through her tears. 'My English is not so good – it's very hard for me.'

'Never mind,' said Avril. 'Maybe we can talk about it tomorrow. You get back into bed now and rest.'

Ludmilla finished the call, and turned to Avril.

Later, Avril saw Dr Sansom.

'Can I call that Russian interpreter, Katya, tomorrow?' she said. 'She was a very nice girl, and perhaps Ludmilla can talk more easily to someone in Russian. And there's the Piano Man too. He said a Russian word, so Katya can try to talk to him again.'

'Good,' Dr Sansom said. 'Very good, Avril. Call me when the interpreter's here. I'd like to come and listen.'

CHAPTER 6

THE SONG

—

Music hurts me, but I cannot stop playing. When I play, I think about her all the time. When I'm not playing, I still think about her. Where is she now? Is she making music, is she sleeping, is she thinking about me . . .?

In the morning Ludmilla talked in Russian on her mobile phone for more than an hour, crying all the time.

'What's this all about?' Dr Sansom asked Avril.

'I don't know,' said Avril. 'I think she's talking to her father in St Petersburg.'

'We need to know her story before we can help her. When is the interpreter coming?'

'At eleven o'clock.'

When she had a moment, Avril went to see the Piano Man and to sit with him for a time. He was nearly always in the patients' sitting room. He sat at the piano, sometimes playing, sometimes just sitting. When Avril talked to him, he listened, but did not speak. His hands moved gently over the piano keys; he answered her with music.

Other patients went in and out of the sitting room, but Doris was always there, in her usual chair.

'Beautiful music,' she said to Avril. 'Beautiful music.'

'Yes, it is,' said Avril. 'Does he talk to you, Doris?'

'He's a nice boy,' Doris said. 'Beautiful music.'

'Very nice,' Avril said. 'But does he say anything? Do you know his name?'

'Yes,' Doris said happily. 'He's the Piano Man. He plays music. Beautiful music.'

'He's the Piano Man,' said Doris happily.
'He plays music. Beautiful music.'

Avril went away, back to her other patients. In Ludmilla's room, it was quiet. Ludmilla lay on her bed, and stared out of the window at the sky.

Avril brought her a hot mug of tea.

'Would you like some tea?' she said in her warm Irish voice. 'Thirsty work, all that talking!'

Ludmilla sat up and took the tea. 'Thank you.'

'Did you talk to your father in St Petersburg?' Avril asked.

Behind her, the door of the room was open, and sounds from the hospital came in.

Suddenly, Ludmilla turned her head, and some of the hot tea went over the bed.

'Hey! Be careful,' said Avril.

But Ludmilla did not hear her. She sat very still.

'What's that?' she whispered.

'What's what?' Avril asked.

'That. That . . . music,' Ludmilla said. 'Where's it coming from?'

'It's a patient. He's playing the piano in the sitting room,' Avril said. 'I think he's—'

'Shh! Listen!' Ludmilla whispered. She put her hand on Avril's arm. 'Listen!'

A second later, she was out of the bed, and running. She ran out of her room, past the other rooms, and along to the patients' sitting room at the end.

Avril ran after her. 'Wait!' she called.

Ludmilla was out of the bed, and running.

At the sitting room door, Ludmilla stopped. She saw the Piano Man at the piano, and her face turned white. She stood, and stared.

The Piano Man heard something, and turned round. He stopped playing, and stared at the girl by the door.

For a long, long minute, nobody moved, nobody spoke. Every sound in the hospital stopped.

Then, very slowly, the Piano Man turned back to the piano, and began to play. He played a slow, beautiful piece of music. For a second or two, Ludmilla did not move or speak. Then she put her head back, closed her eyes, and began to sing.

The song was very sad and very beautiful. Avril did not understand the words, because they were in Russian, but tears came into her eyes. The Piano Man played, and Ludmilla sang. Then, at the end of the song, she walked across the room to him.

The Piano Man stood up and watched her. She came and stood in front of him, and very slowly, very gently, she held out her hand to him.

'Mikhail?' she whispered.

'Lida, Lida, Lida!' said the Piano Man. 'Oh, Lida!'

Then he put his arms around her, and held her for a long time.

Ludmilla held out her hand to him. 'Mikhail?' she whispered.

CHAPTER 7

A RUSSIAN LOVE STORY

—

How strange life is! One minute it is dark, without hope, and the next minute there is wonderful light, and everything can begin again. I am afraid of nothing now – now that I hold Lida in my arms once more . . .

For a long time, maybe two minutes, the Piano Man and Ludmilla stood there, with their arms around each other. Then they began to talk.

They spoke in Russian, very fast, and they didn't stop. They sat down, in two chairs, next to the piano. They held hands, they talked, and laughed, and cried – all at the same time.

'Well! What do you know!' Avril said. She turned to Doris. 'So when he said that word at the piano, it wasn't the word "leader". It was the name of a girl – *Lida*!'

Doris sat in her usual chair, and smiled and nodded. 'Happy people,' she said. 'Happy people.'

'So they are!' said Avril.

She went to find Dr Sansom, and came back to the sitting room with him and Katya the interpreter.

'This is very exciting,' said Dr Sansom. 'Do we know the story yet?'

Katya stared at Ludmilla. 'I think I know her,' she said. 'She's a singer. Ludmilla Terenkova. She's beginning to get famous in Russia, and she's on YouTube a lot. She sings beautiful love songs.'

'Katya, can you talk to them now?' said Avril. 'There's no problem with talking today!'

'Of course,' said Katya. She pulled up a chair, and sat down next to Ludmilla and the Piano Man. They talked in Russian for ten minutes.

'So,' said Katya. She turned to Avril and Dr Sansom. 'It is a love story,' she said, 'with three people. Ludmilla met a young man, Ivan, and when he asked her to marry him, she said yes. But she didn't really love him.'

'Why did she say yes then?' Avril asked.

'I was young,' said Ludmilla. 'I did not know about love. I liked Ivan, yes, but I did not really know him. My father liked him because Ivan is from a rich family. My father is a rich man too, and he wants me to marry money. Money is more important than love, he says.'

The Piano Man said something to Ludmilla in Russian, and she laughed.

'So, why were you on Ivan's boat?' Avril asked.

'For a holiday,' Ludmilla said. 'I didn't want to go, because when Mikhail and I began to work together, everything changed.' She smiled. '*Now*, I know everything about love . . .' She held the Piano Man's hand, and said something to him in Russian.

'Ivan has an expensive boat,' Katya explained. 'He likes expensive things, and he likes to have a beautiful young singer for his fiancée. But he is not a nice man, and Ludmilla knows that now. She is afraid of him. She is afraid of her father too. Mikhail, you see, is from a very poor family. And Ludmilla's father is not going to like that. So, these two young people, very much in love, just wait for an answer to their problem.'

'So how did Mikhail arrive on the beach?' asked Avril.

'Mikhail is a very good pianist,' said Katya, 'and a very good accompanist for Ludmilla – he plays the piano when she sings. Ludmilla wanted to learn some new songs, so she took Mikhail with her on Ivan's boat.'

'It's a very big boat, then, is it?' Avril asked. 'It has a piano on it?'

'Oh yes. These are very rich people.'

'I see. But what did Ivan think about that?'

Avril looked at Ludmilla and Mikhail, holding hands.

'I am a singer,' Ludmilla said, 'and of course I need my accompanist to help me learn new songs. So Mikhail comes with me. Everywhere. Of course.'

'So what happened?' Avril asked.

'This happened,' said Ludmilla. She turned to Mikhail, put her arms around him, and gave him a long, loving kiss. Then she looked at Avril again. 'We were at the back of the boat, but Ivan saw us. He was angry – very, very angry. He hit Mikhail on the head with a bottle,

'Ivan was angry – very, very angry.'

and Mikhail fell into the sea.' Ludmilla stopped. There were tears in her eyes. Mikhail put his arm around her.

'It was so terrible,' Ludmilla said. 'Ivan did not stop the boat, he did not look for Mikhail – he did nothing! It was night, and I could not see Mikhail in the sea. I called and called, but there was no answer.' Tears ran down Ludmilla's face. 'Ivan said, "Too bad, it was an accident." And I told him, "No, you are a murderer!"

'When I opened my eyes again, I was in Falmouth.'

Then he hit me – he hit me on the head, and after that, I knew nothing. When I opened my eyes again, I was in Falmouth. Ivan carried me off the boat, and told a story about an accident at sea – blah, blah, blah! Then he ran away, back to his boat, back to Russia. I never want to see him again.'

Mikhail put his hand on Ludmilla's hair and looked into her eyes. 'He try to kill you, Ludmilla. So – I kill him, with these!' He held up his hands. 'I kill him, with my two hands!'

Ludmilla quickly took Mikhail's hands in hers. 'No, Mikhail, no, no, no! We must forget Ivan now. That is finished . . . done . . . behind us. Now, it is just us, you and me, Mikhail.'

'Well!' said Avril. 'What a story! But now, you're all right?' She looked at Mikhail and smiled. 'Mr Piano Man, are you well now?'

Mikhail smiled back. 'Yes,' he said. 'My English is not good, but yes, I am well. Without Ludmilla, I cannot live. I want to die. So, I do not speak, I have nothing to say. But now . . .' He smiled at Ludmilla.

'But what happens next?' asked Avril. 'And what about Ivan?'

'My father is very angry about Ivan,' said Ludmilla. 'Ivan is his problem now. He's talking to the police in St Petersburg about him. I can go to Italy, my father says, to my grandmother in Verona. She was a singer too.'

She looked at Mikhail and laughed. 'Now I must call my father and tell him about Mikhail – alive and well! And Mikhail can come with me to Italy, yes, Mikhail? There we can make music, beautiful music. Listen . . .'

She pulled Mikhail, laughing, to the piano. Mikhail sat down and began to play, and Ludmilla began to sing.

Suddenly, the room was full of music.

'There we can make music, beautiful music. Listen . . .'

GLOSSARY

accompanist a person who plays music for a singer
beach the land next to the sea
beside next to, at the side of
brain the part inside your head; you use your brain to think
check to look at something/someone to see that it is all right
comfortable (of a chair) nice to sit in
draw (*n* **drawing**) to make a picture with a pen or pencil
fall (past tense **fell**) to go down quickly towards the ground
few/a few some, but not many
fiancé/fiancée the man/woman you are going to marry
gently kindly, quietly, carefully
hold to have something in your hand or your arms
hurt to give someone pain
illegal immigrant a person who comes secretly into a country
     without a passport or the correct papers
injury damage to the body of a person
interpreter a person who translates someone's words into
     another language
key one of the parts of a piano; keys are black or white
kind nice, good, friendly to other people
label a piece of material on something that tells you about it
loud noisy, not quiet
mark a small spot or change of colour on something
marry to take someone as your husband or wife
mental health when a mind is ill or well
mug a big cup
musician a person who plays music
nod to move your head up and down; this often means 'yes'
note a musical sound; a piano key makes one note

nurse a person who takes care of sick people

operation cutting into a person's body to mend something inside

part a small piece of something (e.g. a leg is a part of the body)

patient an ill person in hospital

pianist a person who plays the piano

piano a musical instrument with black and white keys

poor not rich; we also say 'poor' when we feel sorry for someone

press to push something (e.g. a finger on a piano key)

problem something that is difficult, or makes you worry

psychiatric unit a part of a hospital for people with sick minds

really actually, in fact

sad not happy

shake (past tense **shook**) to move your head from side to side, to mean 'no'

shock a sudden, very strong surprise

shout to speak very loudly

sound something that you hear

stare to look at somebody or something for a long time

start to begin

still not moving; also, a word to show something has not changed

strange unusual or surprising

sure knowing that something is true or right

surprise the feeling when something unexpected happens

swim to move in the water

tear water from the eye when a person cries

terrible very bad

try to make an effort to do something

ward a room in a hospital with beds for sick people

whisper to speak very, very quietly

ACTIVITIES

Before Reading

1 Read the back cover of the book, and the introduction on the first page. How much do you know now about the story? Tick one box for each sentence.

	YES	NO
1 Avril works in a hospital.	☐	☐
2 Avril is a doctor.	☐	☐
3 The man on the beach has a very bad injury.	☐	☐
4 An ambulance takes the man to hospital.	☐	☐
5 Avril knows that the man with no name is from St Petersburg.	☐	☐
6 One day the man draws a picture of a boat.	☐	☐

2 What is going to happen in this story? Can you guess? Choose one answer to complete each sentence.

1 The Piano Man does not speak or answer questions . . .
   a) because of an injury to his brain.
   b) because he does not want to.

2 The Piano Man fell into the sea from a boat . . .
   a) because somebody tried to kill him.
   b) because of an accident.

3 This is going to be a love story between . . .
   a) Avril and the Piano Man.
   b) the Piano Man and another patient in the hospital.

While Reading

Read chapters 1 to 3, and then complete these sentences with the best words (one word for each gap).

answer / injury / interpreter / label / piano / psychiatric

1 The man on the beach had an _____ to his head.
2 Everyone asked the man questions but he did not _____.
3 The doctor sent the man to the _____ unit.
4 An _____ came to the hospital and spoke to the man in different languages.
5 The _____ in the man's shirt was Russian.
6 The man drew a picture of a _____.

How much do we know now about the man with no name? Remember to read the man's thoughts at the beginnings of the chapters. Choose Yes (Y), No (N), or Perhaps (P).

1 The man was in a boat before he arrived on the beach.
   Y / N / P
2 Somebody pushed the man off the boat.   Y / N / P
3 The man wants to find somebody called Lida.   Y / N / P
4 The man is very happy.   Y / N / P
5 Lida is the man's sister.   Y / N / P
6 The man's shirt was made in Russia.   Y / N / P
7 The man is Russian.   Y / N / P

Read Chapters 4 and 5. Who says this? Who are they talking to, or about?

1 'You're a musician, aren't you? A pianist.'
2 'Look! He's crying. Poor boy!'
3 '*Spasibo*.'
4 'We've a new patient, a Russian girl.'
5 'Did he come with you to the hospital?'
6 'No. He went back to the boat. He's going back to St Petersburg.'

Before you read Chapter 6, *The Song*, can you guess what is going to happen? Choose as many answers as you like.

1 Ludmilla's father comes to the hospital.
2 Doris finds out the Piano Man's real name.
3 Ludmilla hears piano music in the sitting room.
4 Ivan comes to the hospital and Ludmilla runs away.
5 'Lida' is short for the name 'Ludmilla'.
6 At the end of the chapter we learn the Piano Man's real name.

Before you read Chapter 7, *A Russian Love Story*, how would you like the story to end? Choose your favourite ending.

1 Ludmilla goes back to Ivan in Russia, and the Piano Man stays in England.
2 Ludmilla and the Piano Man go to Italy together to make music.

ACTIVITIES

After Reading

1 **So what happened before the story began? Match these halves of sentences together to make a paragraph.**

1 When Ludmilla agreed to marry Ivan, . . .
2 Ludmilla's father wanted her to marry Ivan . . .
3 Mikhail was on the boat with Ludmilla and Ivan . . .
4 Ivan was already Ludmilla's fiancé . . .
5 The two young people were afraid of Ivan and afraid of Ludmilla's father . . .
6 Ivan was very, very angry . . .
7 He hit Mikhail on the head with a bottle . . .
8 Ludmilla wanted to stop the boat and find Mikhail . . .
9 Ludmilla called Ivan a 'murderer' . . .

10 because he was Ludmilla's accompanist and went everywhere with her.
11 when he saw Mikhail and Ludmilla kissing on the boat.
12 when Ludmilla fell in love with Mikhail.
13 she was young and didn't know anything about love.
14 but Ivan just said, 'Too bad, it was an accident.'
15 so they kept their love secret.
16 and then he hit her on the head too.
17 because Ivan was from a rich family.
18 and Mikhail fell into the sea.

2 Use the clues to complete this crossword with words from the story. Then find the hidden eight-letter word in the crossword.

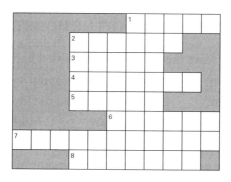

1 You do this when you take someone to be your husband or wife.

2 Both Mikhail and Ludmilla had an _____ to the head because Ivan hit them with a bottle.

3 Someone who works in a hospital and takes care of sick people.

4 A sick person in hospital.

5 When Ludmilla saw Mikhail in the hospital sitting room, it was a big _____ for her.

6 Someone who sings songs.

7 Someone who plays the piano while another person sings.

8 A person who plays the piano.

What is the hidden word? _____

ABOUT THE AUTHOR

Tim Vicary was born in London, but he spent a lot of his childhood in Devon, in the south-west of England. He went to Cambridge University, worked as a schoolteacher, and is now a teaching fellow at the Norwegian Study Centre at the University of York. He is married, has children and grandchildren, and lives in the country in Yorkshire, in the north of England. He enjoys swimming, running, and horse riding.

Tim has written about twenty books for Oxford Bookworms, from Starter level to Stage 3. Other titles at Stage 1 include *The Elephant Man*, *White Death*, *Pocohontas*, *Mary, Queen of Scots*, *The Murder of Mary Jones* (Playscripts), and *Titanic* (Factfiles). *Titanic* won an Extensive Reading Foundation Language Learner Literature Award in 2010, and *The Everest Story* (Factfiles, Stage 3) won another LLL Award in 2011.

Like many writers, Tim gets ideas for his stories from all kinds of places. Many years ago, he read a story in a newspaper about a man with no name who was found on a beach. That is where the idea for *The Piano Man* came from. But the people in this book are very different from the story in the newspaper.

Tim also writes longer novels for adults. His three crime novels, about a tough lady lawyer called Sarah Newby, are *A Game of Proof*, *Fatal Verdict*, and *Bold Counsel*. He has also written four historical novels: *The Blood Upon the Rose*, *Cat and Mouse*, *The Monmouth Summer*, and *Nobody's Slave*. All these books are published as e-books on the Amazon Kindle.

You can read more about Tim and his books on his website <www.timvicary.com>.

OXFORD BOOKWORMS LIBRARY

Classics • Crime & Mystery • Factfiles • Fantasy & Horror
Human Interest • Playscripts • Thriller & Adventure
True Stories • World Stories

The OXFORD BOOKWORMS LIBRARY provides enjoyable reading in English, with a wide range of classic and modern fiction, non-fiction, and plays. It includes original and adapted texts in seven carefully graded language stages, which take learners from beginner to advanced level. An overview is given on the next pages.

All Stage 1 titles are available as audio recordings, as well as over eighty other titles from Starter to Stage 6. All Starters and many titles at Stages 1 to 4 are specially recommended for younger learners. Every Bookworm is illustrated, and Starters and Factfiles have full-colour illustrations.

The OXFORD BOOKWORMS LIBRARY also offers extensive support. Each book contains an introduction to the story, notes about the author, a glossary, and activities. Additional resources include tests and worksheets, and answers for these and for the activities in the books. There is advice on running a class library, using audio recordings, and the many ways of using Oxford Bookworms in reading programmes. Resource materials are available on the website <www.oup.com/bookworms>.

The *Oxford Bookworms Collection* is a series for advanced learners. It consists of volumes of short stories by well-known authors, both classic and modern. Texts are not abridged or adapted in any way, but carefully selected to be accessible to the advanced student.

You can find details and a full list of titles in the *Oxford Bookworms Library Catalogue* and *Oxford English Language Teaching Catalogues*, and on the website <www.oup.com/bookworms>.

THE OXFORD BOOKWORMS LIBRARY
GRADING AND SAMPLE EXTRACTS

STARTER • 250 HEADWORDS

present simple – present continuous – imperative –
can/cannot, must – *going to* (future) – simple gerunds …

Her phone is ringing – but where is it?

Sally gets out of bed and looks in her bag. No phone. She looks under the bed. No phone. Then she looks behind the door. There is her phone. Sally picks up her phone and answers it. *Sally's Phone*

STAGE 1 • 400 HEADWORDS

… past simple – coordination with *and*, *but*, *or* –
subordination with *before, after, when, because, so* …

I knew him in Persia. He was a famous builder and I worked with him there. For a time I was his friend, but not for long. When he came to Paris, I came after him – I wanted to watch him. He was a very clever, very dangerous man. *The Phantom of the Opera*

STAGE 2 • 700 HEADWORDS

… present perfect – *will* (future) – (*don't*) *have to, must not, could* –
comparison of adjectives – simple *if* clauses – past continuous –
tag questions – *ask/tell* + infinitive …

While I was writing these words in my diary, I decided what to do. I must try to escape. I shall try to get down the wall outside. The window is high above the ground, but I have to try. I shall take some of the gold with me – if I escape, perhaps it will be helpful later. *Dracula*

STAGE 3 • 1000 HEADWORDS

... should, may – present perfect continuous – *used to* – past perfect –
causative – relative clauses – indirect statements ...

Of course, it was most important that no one should see
Colin, Mary, or Dickon entering the secret garden. So Colin
gave orders to the gardeners that they must all keep away
from that part of the garden in future. *The Secret Garden*

STAGE 4 • 1400 HEADWORDS

... past perfect continuous – passive (simple forms) –
would conditional clauses – indirect questions –
relatives with *where/when* – gerunds after prepositions/phrases ...

I was glad. Now Hyde could not show his face to the world
again. If he did, every honest man in London would be proud
to report him to the police. *Dr Jekyll and Mr Hyde*

STAGE 5 • 1800 HEADWORDS

... future continuous – future perfect –
passive (modals, continuous forms) –
would have conditional clauses – modals + perfect infinitive ...

If he had spoken Estella's name, I would have hit him. I was so
angry with him, and so depressed about my future, that I could
not eat the breakfast. Instead I went straight to the old house.
Great Expectations

STAGE 6 • 2500 HEADWORDS

... passive (infinitives, gerunds) – advanced modal meanings –
clauses of concession, condition

When I stepped up to the piano, I was confident. It was as if I
knew that the prodigy side of me really did exist. And when I
started to play, I was so caught up in how lovely I looked that
I didn't worry how I would sound. *The Joy Luck Club*

BOOKWORMS · TRUE STORIES · STAGE 1

Pocahontas

Retold by Tim Vicary

A beautiful young Indian girl, and a brave Englishman. Black eyes, and blue eyes. A friendly smile, a laugh, a look of love . . . But this is North America in 1607, and love is not easy. The girl is the daughter of King Powhatan, and the Englishman is a white man. And the Indians of Virginia do not want the white men in their beautiful country.

This is the famous story of Pocahontas, and her love for the Englishman John Smith.

BOOKWORMS · THRILLER & ADVENTURE · STAGE 1

White Death

TIM VICARY

Sarah Harland is nineteen, and she is in prison. At the airport, they find heroin in her bag. So, now she is waiting to go to court. If the court decides that it was her heroin, then she must die.

She says she did not do it. But if she did not, who did? Only two people can help Sarah: her mother, and an old boyfriend who does not love her now. Can they work together? Can they find the real criminal before it is too late?